The fun way to learn!

Razzamajazz
clarinet

SARAH WATTS

Kevin
Mayhew

We hope you enjoy *Razzamajazz for Clarinet*.
Further copies of this and our many other books are available
from your local Kevin Mayhew stockist.

In case of difficulty, please contact the publisher direct by writing to:

The Sales Department
KEVIN MAYHEW LTD
Buxhall
Stowmarket
Suffolk IP14 3BW

Phone 01449 737978
Fax 01449 737834
E-mail info@kevinmayhewltd.com

Please ask for our complete catalogue of outstanding
Piano and Instrumental Music.

First published in Great Britain in 2001 by Kevin Mayhew Ltd.

© Copyright 2001 Kevin Mayhew Ltd.

ISBN I 84003 717 2
ISMN M 57004 854 0
Catalogue No: 3611571

0 1 2 3 4 5 6 7 8 9

Cover design: Jonathan Stroulger
Music setter: Kate Gallaher
Proof reader: Marian Hellen

Printed and bound in Great Britain

Contents

A note from the composer

This is a fun book of jazzy pieces with a 'feel good' accompaniment to encourage you in the early stages of learning.

Although *Razzamajazz* is not a tutor, I hope you will enjoy learning the pieces and benefit from them.

SARAH WATTS

Introducing E

This is where it goes on the music

To play E cover the holes coloured black

Left hand

Right hand

EASY DOES IT

NOTE USED - E

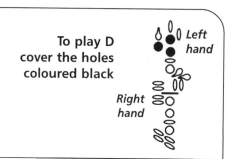

To play D
cover the holes
coloured black

This is where it goes on the music

TWO AT TWILIGHT

NOTES USED - E, D

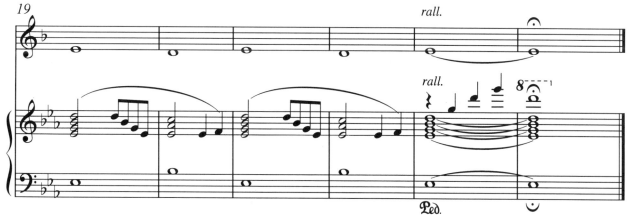

now for C

This is where it goes on the music

To play C
cover the holes
coloured black

Left hand

Right hand

STARDOM WALTZ

NOTES USED - E, D, C

6

for and with Daniel Cashman

STRIPY CAT CRAWL

NOTES USED - E, D

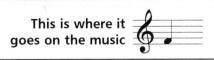

...and now F

This is where it
goes on the music

To play F
cover the hole
coloured black

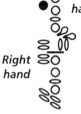

Right
hand

MR COOL

NOTES USED - E, D, C, F

Swing ($\downarrow$ = 130)

Optional vocals (spoken):

Yeh!   U - huh!

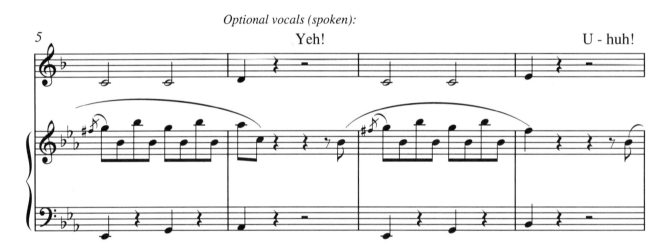

Hit it!   That's cool!

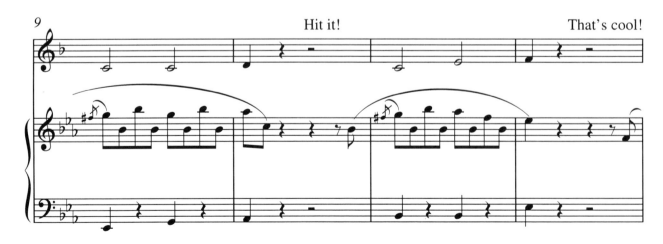

Yeh!   U - huh!

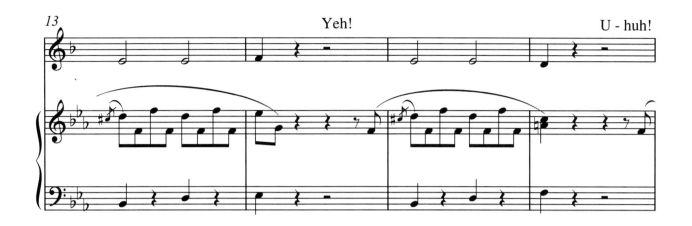

Hit it!   I'm done!

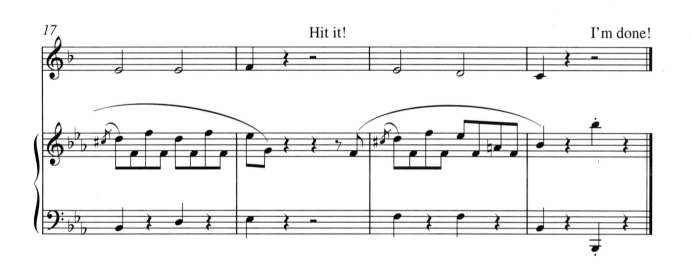

11

KIM'S BALLAD

NOTES USED - E, D, C, F

and next G

This is where it goes on the music

To play G you do not need to cover any holes

Left hand

Right hand

MOVIE BUSTER

NOTES USED - E, D, C, F, G

Driving ($\bullet = 150$)

MELLOW OUT

NOTES USED - E, D, C, F, G

This is where it goes on the music

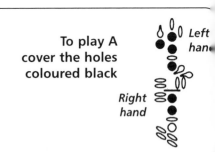

WATER LILIES

NOTES USED - E, D, C, F, G, A

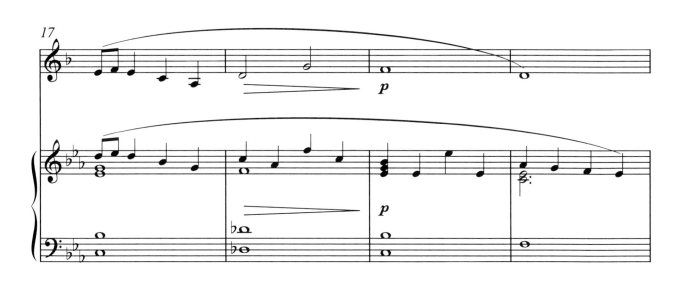

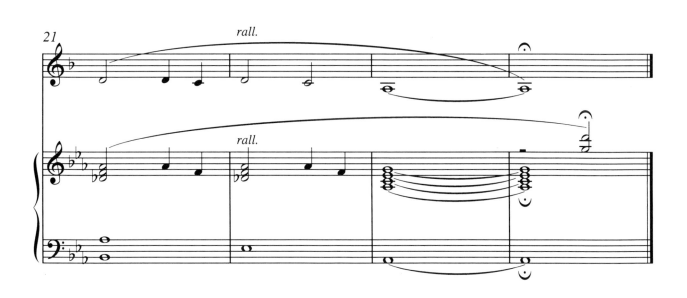

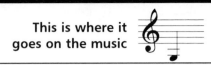

here's low G

This is where it goes on the music

To play low G cover the holes coloured black

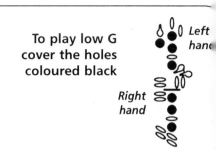

Left hand

Right hand

TEN TOE TAPPER

NOTES USED - E, D, C, F, G, A, low G

Swing ($\quarternote$ = 158)

© Copyright 2001 Kevin Mayhew Ltd.
It is illegal to photocopy music.

20

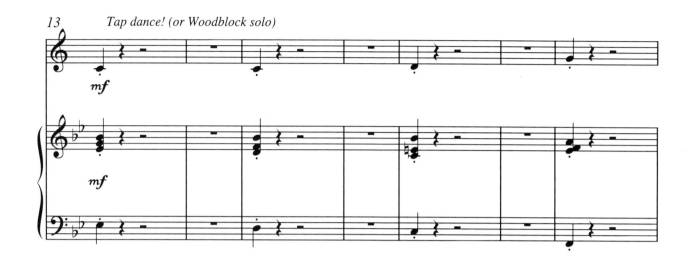

Tap dance! (or Woodblock solo)

now for B♭

This is where it goes on the music

To play B♭ cover the holes coloured black

Left hand

Right hand

PLAY OF LIGHT

NOTES USED - E, D, C, F, G, A, low G, B♭

SEA SPARKLE

NOTES USED - E, D, C, F, G, A, B♭

...and now E♭

This is where it goes on the music

MORNING IN MOSCOW

NOTES USED - D, C, F, A, low G, B♭, E♭

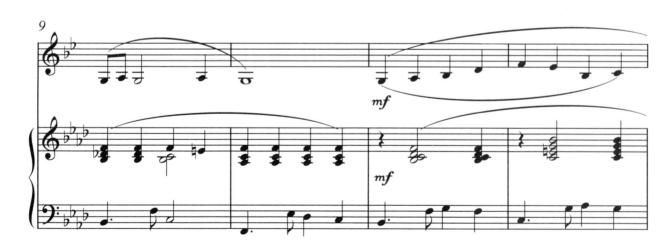

and finally B

This is where it goes on the music

To play B cover the holes coloured black

Left hand

Right hand

SHRIMP SHUFFLE

NOTES USED - E, D, C, F, G, A, low G, Bb, Eb, B

Cool and laid back (♩ = 110)

Last time to Coda

Last time to Coda

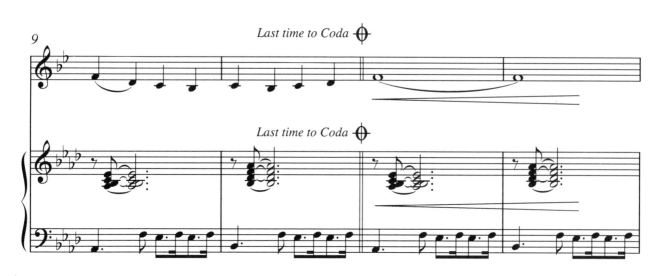

BANANA TANGO

NOTES USED - E, D, C, F, G, A, B♭, B

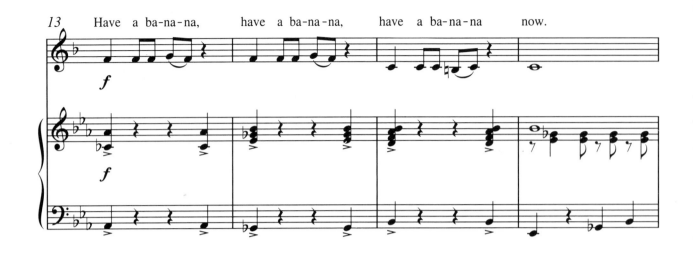

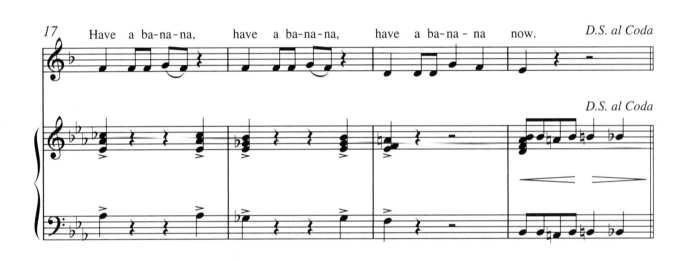